AT THE FEET OF SHIVA

NEITHER THE BROADEST...
...NOR THE TALLEST OF MOUNTAINS COULD STOP ITS PROGRESS ONCE RAVANA HAD WILLED IT TO MOVE.
HIGHER! HIGHER!
FLY OVER IT!
THE CHARIOT OBEYED HIS EVERY WISH.

THEN ONE DAY, AS THEY WERE FLYING TOWARDS MOUNT KAILAS, THE ABODE OF SHIVA, THE CHARIOT SUDDENLY STOPPED.
WHY DOESN'T PUSHPAKA OBEY ME? THIS IS SURELY THE WORK OF SOME BEING ON THE MOUNTAIN.

TRY AS HE MIGHT, RAVANA COULD NOT GET IT TO MOVE.
WELL, IF PUSHPAKA WILL NOT FLY OVER THE MOUNTAIN, I WILL LIFT THE MOUNTAIN AND TOSS IT OUT OF MY WAY.

ATOP THE MOUNTAIN, AT THAT MOMENT, PARVATI, WHO HAD JUST HAD A TIFF WITH SHIVA, WAS WALKING AWAY IN A HUFF.
PARVATI...

COME BACK, PARVATI!
I WILL NEVER COME BACK.

PARVATI!

SUDDENLY, THE EARTH SHOOK...

... AND HUGE BOULDERS CAME TUMBLING DOWN.

PARVATI LOST HER BALANCE ...

... AND ALMOST FELL.
SHE STEADIED HERSELF, HOWEVER...

...AND RAN ...

... INTO THE ARMS OF SHIVA.
WH-WH- WHAT ... WH- WH- WHO- WHO...

IT WAS RAVANA LIFTING THE MOUNTAIN, NONE ELSE.

SHIVA ! IT'S HAPPENING AGAIN ! THE MOUNTAIN...

SHIVA, PLEASE... PLEASE STOP THIS TERRIFYING TREMOR.

SHIVA STOOD UP...

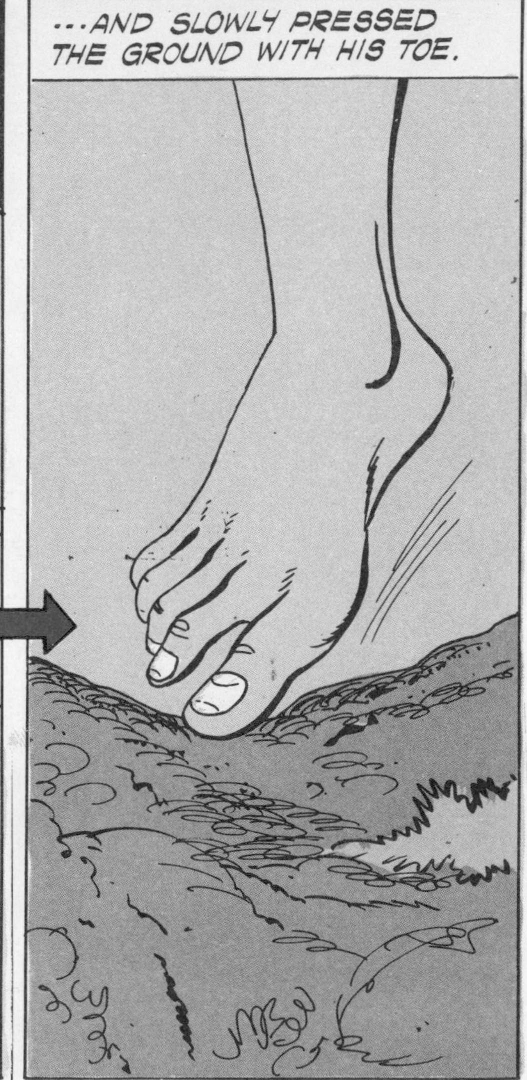
...AND SLOWLY PRESSED THE GROUND WITH HIS TOE.

AND THE NEXT MOMENT ...

...THE MOUNTAIN CAME DOWN ON RAVANA'S HANDS.

HE LET OUT A THUNDEROUS ROAR.

WHAT IS THAT ?
AAAAAHH!

IT IS THE CRY OF OUR FRIEND. THE ONE WHO CAUSED THE TREMOR THAT BROUGHT YOU BACK TO ME.

HE WAS LIFTING MOUNT KAILAS.
WHAT A COURAGEOUS BEING! FORGIVE HIM, MY LORD.

SOON—
THE BEING ON THIS MOUNTAIN IS MORE POWERFUL THAN I.

IF ONLY HE WOULD APPEAR BEFORE ME.
RAVANA, I SHIVA, AM PLEASED BY YOUR COURAGE AND PERSEVERANCE.

LORD SHIVA!

ARISE, RAVANA.

TO SHOW YOU HOW PLEASED I AM...

...I GIVE YOU CHANDRAHASA, MY INVINCIBLE SWORD.

RAVANA TOOK THE SWORD, BOWED TO SHIVA, ASCENDED HIS CHARIOT AND FLEW OFF.

THE MAHISHMATI EPISODE

ONCE AS RAVANA WAS ROAMING AROUND IN PUSHPAKA, WITH A FEW OF HIS MINISTERS, THEY CAME TO MAHISHMATI, THE KINGDOM OF KARTAVEERYA ARJUNA.
THE NARMADA! I WILL LAND ON THE BANK OF THIS HOLY RIVER.

WHAT A BEAUTIFUL SPOT!

I SHALL BATHE IN THE RIVER AND WORSHIP SHIVA BEFORE WE MOVE ON.

SO—

KARTAVEERYA ARJUNA HAD CHOSEN THE SAME HOUR, BUT A SPOT MUCH FARTHER AWAY, TO SPORT IN THE RIVER WITH HIS WIVES.

MY LORD, WE AGREE THAT YOU ARE VERY STRONG. BUT CAN YOU CONTAIN NARMADA?
NO ONE CAN!

NOT EVEN YOU, THE THOUSAND-ARMED ARJUNA.
I'LL TAKE UP THE CHALLENGE!

ARJUNA SAT ON THE BED OF THE RIVER AND STRETCHED OUT HIS ARMS.

SOON, BEHIND ARJUNA THE BED OF THE RIVER RAN DRY...

...WHILE IN FRONT OF HIM THE WATER-LEVEL ROSE...
...AND THE RIVER OVERFLOWED ITS BANKS, SUBMERGING THE SURROUNDING LAND.

*SHIVA IS WORSHIPPED IN THIS FORM

CONTD. ON PAGE 19

RAVANA THE MIGHTY

Script: Swarn Khandpur
Illustrated by: S.K. Parab

RAVANA, THE RAKSHASA KING OF LANKA, WAS A MIGHTY BEING. HIS STRENGTH WAS SO GREAT THAT HE COULD AGITATE THE SEAS AND SPLIT THE PEAKS OF MOUNTAINS.

ON THE BATTLEFIELD OF LANKA, RAMA WHO WAS SEEING HIM FOR THE FIRST TIME, EXCLAIMED, "AH! WHAT GLORY, WHAT EXCEEDING MAJESTY IS RAVANA'S! AS ONE CANNOT GAZE ON THE SUN, NEITHER CAN THE EYE REST ON HIM, SUCH IS THE BLINDING POWER OF HIS MAGNIFICENCE! NEITHER DEVAS, DANAVAS NOR HEROES POSSESS A BODY EQUAL TO HIS!"

RAMA AND RAVANA WERE SKILLED WARRIORS AND BOTH BROUGHT EXCEPTIONAL KNOWLEDGE IN THE SCIENCE OF ARMS TO THE FIGHT. WATCHING THE DREADFUL COMBAT BETWEEN THE TWO, THE DEVAS, THE GANDHARVAS, THE RISHIS, THE DANAVAS AND THE DAITYAS CRIED OUT, "AS THE SKY IS COMPARABLE ONLY WITH THE SKY AND THE OCEAN ONLY WITH THE OCEAN, SO IS THIS FIGHT BETWEEN RAMA AND RAVANA!"

RAMA'S VICTORY OVER RAVANA IS COMMEMORATED IN THE NORTH DURING THE FESTIVAL OF DUSSEHRA. FOR NINE DAYS RAMLILA IS ENACTED AND ON THE TENTH DAY, DUSSEHRA WHICH MARKS THE DAY OF VICTORY, AN EFFIGY OF RAVANA IS BURNT.

THE HUGE EFFIGY IS ERECTED ON A MIGHTY FRAMEWORK OF BAMBOOS. IT IS THEN FILLED WITH FIRE-CRACKERS AND COVERED ON THE OUTSIDE WITH COLOURED PAPERS.

ALTHOUGH RAVANA IS DESCRIBED IN THE RAMAYANA AS HAVING TEN HEADS, IN FOLK ART HE IS OFTEN SHOWN WITH ONLY NINE.

ON DUSSEHRA DAY, WHEN THE EFFIGY CATCHES FIRE, IT BLAZES IN FIERY SPLENDOUR TILL THE MIGHTY RAVANA FALLS.

THE MINISTERS WATCHED HELPLESSLY AS THE WATER GRADUALLY NEARED RAVANA.

AS IT BEGAN TO WASH AWAY THE LINGA, RAVANA'S PRAYERS ENDED AND HE OPENED HIS EYES.

THE RIVER SEEMS TO BE IN FLOOD, MASTER.

GO AND FIND OUT WHY.

SOON, THE MINISTER WAS BACK.
MASTER, A MIGHTY BEING HAS DAMMED THE RIVER WITH HIS MASSIVE TRUNK AND HIS ONE THOUSAND ARMS!

ONE THOUSAND ARMS! IT IS KARTAVEERYA ARJUNA!

HOW DARE HE!

HE SHALL MEET HIS END TODAY! LEAD ME TO HIM.

SO—
LOOK! MASTER! THERE HE IS!

ARJUNA! IF YOU MUST PROVE YOUR STRENGTH, PROVE IT IN COMBAT WITH ME. NOT BY THROTTLING A HOLY RIVER!

AS ARJUNA STOOD UP NARMADA SLID BACK INTO HER BED AND RUSHED DOWNSTREAM.

ARJUNA STRODE OVER TO RAVANA.

WE AT MAHISHMATI ARE VERY HOSPITABLE TO OUR GUESTS. WE GIVE THEM WHATEVER THEY DESIRE.

SO I WILL GIVE YOU THE BATTLE YOU CRAVE.

THE WEAPON THEY CHOSE WAS THE MACE. THE TWO MIGHTY KINGS FOUGHT LONG AND HARD.

AT LAST A BLOW FROM ARJUNA SENT RAVANA REELING...
THUD

...TO THE GROUND.

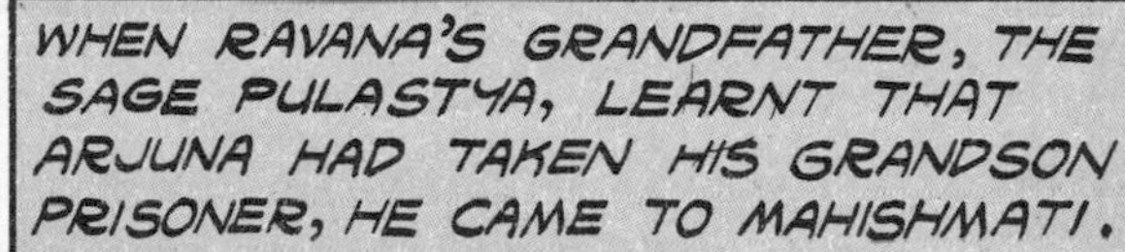
WHEN RAVANA'S GRANDFATHER, THE SAGE PULASTYA, LEARNT THAT ARJUNA HAD TAKEN HIS GRANDSON PRISONER, HE CAME TO MAHISHMATI.

WELCOME, REVERED ONE!

TELL ME
HOW BEST
I CAN SERVE
YOU ?

ARJUNA, YOU HAVE PROVED THAT NONE IS EQUAL TO YOU IN STRENGTH BY SUBDUING RAVANA.

NOW RELEASE MY GRANDSON.
AS YOU COMMAND, REVERED ONE.

ARJUNA SET RAVANA FREE, HONOURED HIM WITH GIFTS AND SEALED THEIR FRIENDSHIP WITH FIRE AS THE WITNESS.

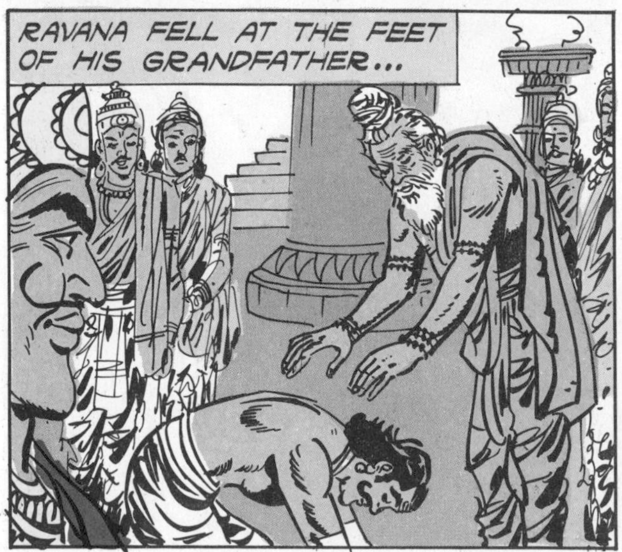
RAVANA FELL AT THE FEET OF HIS GRANDFATHER...

...AND LEFT MAHISHMATI WITH HIS MINISTERS.

TAILPIECE

ONE DAY RAVANA CAME TO THE CITY OF KISHKINDHA.
AH! THERE'S VALI, THE MONKEY KING. I WILL LAND HERE.

PUSHPAKA DUTIFULLY BROUGHT HIM DOWN AND RAVANA WALKED OUT.

SURELY, THE PUNY CREATURE SAW ME LAND. WHY DIDN'T HE GREET ME ?

HE NEEDS TO BE HUMBLED FOR THIS.

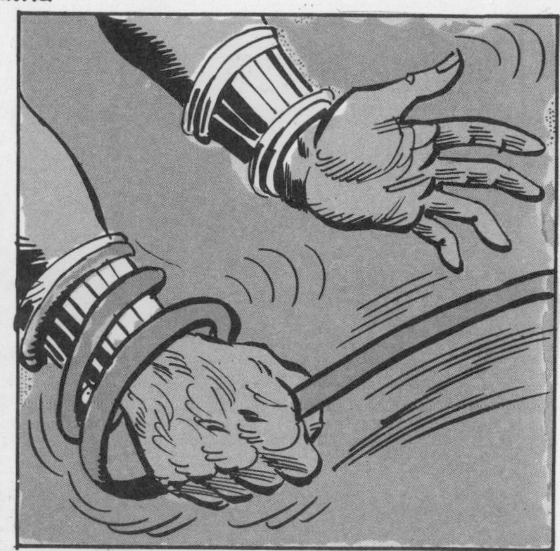

!!

SUDDENLY—
HEY!

VALI, THE MONKEY KING, HAD FINISHED HIS PRAYER ON THE EASTERN SHORE. HE WAS NOW OFF...

...TO THE WESTERN SHORE...

...FOR A HOLY DIP...
SPLASH

...AND MORE PRAYERS.

NOW IS THE TIME TO FREE MYSELF.

!

VALI TOOK OFF AGAIN.

AFTER PRAYING IN THE HIMALAYAS HE CAME DOWN TO THE SOUTHERN SHORE...

...FOR THE LAST DIP...
SPLASH

...AND THE LAST ROUND OF PRAYERS.

I MUST FREE MYSELF BEFORE HE LEAPS OFF AGAIN !

USING ALL HIS MIGHT, RAVANA KICKED OUT WITH HIS ONLY FREE LEG.

BUT—
NO!

VALI TOOK OFF AGAIN.

THIS TIME HE WAS ON HIS WAY HOME TO KISHKINDHA.

HELP! LET ME GO! LET ME GO!

SOMEBODY IS IN DISTRESS. BUT I DON'T SEE ANYONE.

WHERE ARE YOU?
HERE!

VALI SPUN ROUND—
WHERE?

HERE! HERE!

VALI SPUN ROUND AGAIN.
SOMEBODY IS TRYING TO MAKE A FOOL OF ME!

COME OUT, WHOEVER YOU ARE ?
I CAN'T. I AM CAUGHT IN YOUR TAIL.

OH !

VALI UNCOILED HIS TAIL.

YOU ! THE KING OF LANKA ! HOW DID YOU...

LATER—
HOW DID IT HAPPEN ?
IT WAS AN ACCIDENT. LET US FORGET IT.

VALI TREATED HIS ROYAL GUEST WITH RESPECT. LATER RAVANA, SWEARING ETERNAL FRIENDSHIP WITH VALI, SET OFF FOR LANKA.

AMAR
CHITRA
KATHA